Let's face it, Charlie Brown!

Charles M. Schulz

CORONET BOOKS
Hodder Fawcett, London

First published by Fawcett Publications Inc.,
New York

Coronet edition 1968
Eleventh impression 1979

Printed in Great Britain for Hodder
Fawcett Ltd., Mill Road, Dunton Green,
Sevenoaks, Kent (Editorial Office:
47 Bedford Square, London, WC1 3DP) by
C. Nicholls & Company Ltd
The Philips Park Press, Manchester

ISBN 0 340 04294 X

..AND THEN SHE SAID, "LINUS."... THAT'S JUST THE WAY SHE SAID IT..."LINUS."....SHE CAME RIGHT OUT, AND SAID MY NAME JUST AS PLAIN AS DAY...

YOU ALWAYS OVERDO THINGS!

IT'S ALL RIGHT TO LIKE A TEACHER, BUT IT'S WRONG TO WORSHIP HER!

I NEVER SAID I WORSHIP HER...

I JUST SAID THAT I'M VERY FOND OF THE GROUND ON WHICH SHE WALKS!
SCHULZ

YOU SAY MISS OTHMAR IS ONLY HUMAN...WELL, I SAY SHE'S MORE!

LIKE ALL GOOD TEACHERS, SHE HAS IN HER BEING A TOUCH OF THE SPIRIT FIRED BY THE DEDICATION OF HER CALLING!

SNIF

FORGIVE ME FOR CRYING, BUT THAT'S ONE OF THE MOST MOVING SPEECHES I'VE EVER HEARD...
SCHULZ

?
OH, MISS OTHMAR! WHY, MISS OTHMAR!

DON'T EVEN SAY THINGS LIKE THAT, MISS OTHMAR...WHY, MISS OTHMAR!
I CAN'T STAND IT! I JUST CAN'T STAND IT!
SCHULZ

THE WAY I SEE IT AS SOON AS A BABY IS BORN, HE SHOULD BE ISSUED A BANJO!

SCHULZ

SOMETIMES I LIE AWAKE AT NIGHT WONDERING WHY I WAS BORN..

WHY WAS I PUT ON THIS EARTH? WHAT AM I DOING HERE?

..AND THEN SUDDENLY IT HITS ME..

I HAVEN'T GOT THE SLIGHTEST IDEA!
SCHULZ

DO YOU WANT TO HEAR SOMETHING CUTE THAT MY LITTLE SISTER DID YESTERDAY?

OFFHAND, CHARLIE BROWN, I CAN THINK OF NOTHING THAT WOULD BORE ME MORE!

DON'T WORRY, I'M NOT EVEN GOING TO TRY TO TELL YOU!!
SCHULZ

HOW'S SALLY, CHARLIE BROWN?
SHE'S FINE, THANK YOU..

I'M GLAD YOU MENTIONED HER BECAUSE SHE DID SOME-THING KIND OF CUTE YESTERDAY, AND I'D LIKE TO TELL..

VIOLET, WOULD YOU CARE TO HEAR SOMETHING CUTE THAT SALLY DID YESTERDAY?

SALLY IS MY LITTLE BABY SISTER, YOU KNOW...

MY NAME IS CHARLIE BROWN!
SCHULZ

SCHROEDER, WOULD YOU LIKE TO HEAR SOMETHING CUTE THAT SALLY DID YESTERDAY?

SURE...I'D BE GLAD TO...
WELL, IT WAS LIKE THIS... SHE WAS..

SCHULZ

LINUS! SUPPERTIME! MOTHER SAYS COME RIGHT IN..

OKAY, I'LL BE THERE AS SOON AS I FINISH THIS ROAD...
MOTHER SAYS TO COME IN RIGHT NOW, AND SHE MEANS RIGHT NOW!

SIGH
YOU CAN'T FIGHT CITY HALL!

I CAN NEVER GO ANYPLACE WITH ANOTHER PERSON BECAUSE THAT PERSON USUALLY DOESN'T LIKE ME...

IF I'M WITH **TWO** OTHER PEOPLE, I ALWAYS FEEL THAT THEY'RE TALKING ABOUT ME WHENEVER I HAPPEN TO TURN MY BACK...

IF I'M WITH **THREE** PEOPLE, I ALWAYS HAVE THE FEELING THAT THEY DON'T REALLY NEED ME... I GUESS THAT'S WHY I'M USUALLY...

..ALONE!
SCHULZ

I'M INCLINED TO AGREE WITH YOU, CHARLIE BROWN..
BUT ON THE OTHER HAND WE MUST BE CAUTIOUS IN OUR THINKING...

WE MUST BE CAREFUL NOT TO "THROW OUT THE BABY WITH THE BATH"
PLEASE PARDON THE EXPRESSION
SCHULZ

BLAUGH!!

CHLORINE!
SCHULZ

YOU'RE WEAK, YOU'RE HOMELY, YOU'RE STUPID, YOU'RE...
NOW, WAIT A MINUTE! IT'S ONLY EIGHT O'CLOCK IN THE MORNING...YOU'RE STARTING IN ON ME KIND OF EARLY, AREN'T YOU?

I CAN'T HELP IT, CHARLIE BROWN...
YOU HAVE SO MANY FAULTS IT TAKES A WHOLE DAY TO LIST THEM!

HI, "PIG-PEN"... YOU LOOK PRETTY CLEAN TODAY FOR A CHANGE
WELL, IT'S A PROBLEM, CHARLIE BROWN..

I'M CLEAN NOW, BUT I DON'T KNOW HOW LONG IT WILL LAST..

!

YOU CAN SEE WHAT I'M UP AGAINST!
SCHULZ

BOY, IF I WERE A LEAF, I WOULDN'T BE SO ANXIOUS TO LEAVE HOME..

I'D STICK TO THAT OL' TREE JUST AS LONG AS I COULD!

SEE, SMARTY? WHAT DID IT GET YOU?

I THINK LEAVES ARE CRAZY!

THEY ALL SEEM SO ANXIOUS TO FALL OFF THE TREE LIKE SOMEONE WHO CAN HARDLY WAIT TO GET AWAY FROM HOME

BOY, IF I WERE A LEAF, THEY'D NEVER GET ME OUT OF THE TREE! I'D WHIMPER AND WHINE AND BEG FOR MERCY...

I'D PROBABLY EMBARRASS THE WHOLE TREE!
SCHULZ

WELL! THE FIRST FALLING LEAF OF THE SEASON...

THE FIRST LEAF TO MAKE THE COURAGEOUS LEAP! THE FIRST LEAF TO DEPART FROM HOME! THE FIRST LEAF TO PLUNGE INTO THE UNKNOWN!

THE FIRST LEAF TO DIE!!
SCHULZ

HI, LEAF!
SCHULZ

IF I WERE A LEAF, YOU'D NEVER CATCH ME FALLING OFF A TREE!

I'D HANG ON FOR DEAR LIFE! I'D STAY WITH THAT TREE UNTIL THEY CAME TO GET ME!
EVEN THEN THEY'D HAVE TO DRAG ME OFF! I'D KICK AND SCREAM, AND PUT UP A REAL FIGHT!

I'D MAKE A LOUSY LEAF!
SCHULZ

WELL! I'M GLAD TO SEE THERE'S ONE SMART LEAF IN THE CROWD!
I'M GLAD TO SEE THAT SOMEONE HAS SENSE ENOUGH TO STAY PUT!
!
SIGH
SCHULZ

SCHULZ

WOW!
WHATS THE MATTER? IS IT SNOWING?
BOY, I'LL SAY IT'S SNOWING!
IT'S PITCH WHITE OUTSIDE!
SCHULZ

SNOOPY! SUPPERTIME!

ALL RIGHT, IF YOU DON'T WANT YOUR SUPPER, I'LL GIVE IT TO THE CAT NEXT DOOR!

THAT USUALLY DOES IT!
SCHULZ

CHARLIE BROWN I THINK YOU SHOULD RESOLVE TO BE PERFECT DURING THE COMING YEAR...
PERFECT? GOOD GRIEF NOBODY'S PERFECT! WHAT DO YOU EXPECT OF ME?
I THINK YOU **CAN** BE IF YOU TRY.. I REALLY DO!

ALL RIGHT, LUCY, IF YOU HAVE THAT MUCH FAITH IN ME, I'LL TRY! I HEREBY RESOLVE TO BE PERFECT DURING THE NEXT YEAR!
YOU? PERFECT?!
HA! HA! HA! HA!
SCHULZ

SO YOU REALLY LIKE YOUR TEACHER, EH, LINUS?

SHE'S A GOOD TEACHER, CHARLIE BROWN...NO, SHE'S MORE THAN JUST A GOOD TEACHER..SHE'S A GREAT HUMAN BEING!

NO, SHE'S MORE THAN A GOOD TEACHER AND A GREAT HUMAN BEING...

MISS OTHMAR IS A GOOD TEACHER, A GREAT HUMAN BEING AND A LIVING DOLL!!
SCHULZ

FLOWERS FOR THE TEACHER, EH, LINUS?
YOU'LL NEVER GET ANYWHERE WITH MISS OTHMAR BY USING BRIBERY..
BRIBERY? THIS ISN'T BRIBERY...
I PREFER TO THINK OF IT AS PUMP-PRIMING!
SCHULZ

LINUS SAID THAT MISS OTHMAR REALLY SPOKE OUT AGAINST BLANKETS TODAY...

SHE SAID THAT IF A CHILD DRAGGED A BLANKET AROUND WITH HIM, IT WAS A SIGN OF IMMATURITY, AND SHE SAID THAT SHE WOULD NEVER PUT UP WITH THAT!

WOW!! THAT MEANS HE'S GOING TO HAVE TO CHOOSE BETWEEN HIS BLANKET AND MISS OTHMAR, DOESN'T IT?

WHO'S MISS OTHMAR?
SCHULZ

BUTTERFLIES LIKE ME!
SCHULZ

BOY, I'M GLAD I'M NOT A LIZARD..

YOU HANG AROUND MINDING YOUR OWN BUSINESS WHEN ALL OF A SUDDEN SOME KID COMES ALONG, AND WHAM! THERE YOU ARE...

TRAPPED INSIDE A BOTTLE!
SCHULZ

EVERYONE'S SO NERVOUS THESE DAYS..

EVERYONE YOU TALK TO SEEMS TO BE JUMPY..

ISN'T THAT RIGHT, SNOOPY?

AAAUGH!
SCHULZ

I SUPPOSE YOU WOULDN'T CARE TO PLAY "ROCK-A-BYE, BABY" FOR MY LITTLE SISTER HERE, JUST AS A FAVOR, WOULD YOU?

IT'S A SHAME THAT IT HAS TO SNOW ONLY IN THE WINTER..
IF IT SNOWED IN THE SUMMER, A PERSON COULD STAY OUTSIDE LONGER, AND ENJOY IT MORE...
WELL, I'LL SAY ONE THING FOR YOU...
THE QUALITY OF YOUR STUPIDITY IS RISING!
SCHULZ

THIS, LINUS, IS A PICTURE OF THE HUMAN HEART!

ONE SIDE IS FILLED WITH HATE AND THE OTHER SIDE IS FILLED WITH LOVE...

THESE ARE THE TWO FORCES WHICH ARE CONSTANTLY AT WAR WITH EACH OTHER...

I THINK I KNOW JUST WHAT YOU MEAN...I CAN FEEL THEM FIGHTING!
SCHULZ

LUCY SAYS THAT HALF OF OUR HEART IS FILLED WITH HATE AND HALF IS FILLED WITH LOVE...

AND SHE SAYS THIS HATE AND LOVE ARE ALWAYS FIGHTING WITHIN US...ALWAYS QUARRELING, BATTLING, STRUGGLING....

PEACE!
SCHULZ

LUCY, I DON'T **WANT** MY HEART TO BE HALF LOVE AND HALF HATE..

I WANT TO BE ALL LOVE!
GOOD FOR YOU, LINUS...ALL YOU HAVE TO DO IS LEAN A LITTLE TO ONE SIDE....
?

SEE? NOW THE LOVE WILL GET A CHANCE TO SPILL OVER INTO THE HATE!
GOOD GRIEF!
SCHULZ

EVERY NOW AND THEN YOU RUN INTO A KITE WITH A MIND OF ITS OWN!
SCHULZ

I THINK A NICE SMILE ENHANCES ANY PERSONALITY

THAT'S TRUE ...THERE REALLY IS NOTHING MORE ATTRACTIVE THAN A NICE SMILE

WITHIN BOUNDS OF REASON, OF COURSE
OF COURSE
SCHULZ

DO YOU WANT THE REST OF THIS SANDWICH, SNOOPY?

I'VE ALREADY EATEN HALF OF IT.... YOU DON'T MIND?

OKAY, IT'S YOURS..
I'M SO HUMBLE IT'S SICKENING!
SCHULZ

RATS!
I FORGOT THE EGG SHELLS!

MISS OTHMAR WANTED US TO BRING SOME EGG SHELLS TO SCHOOL TODAY...WE WERE GOING TO MAKE IGLI...

IGLI?
THAT'S PLURAL, CHARLIE BROWN..

ONE IGLOO...TWO IGLI!
SCHULZ

GOOD GRIEF! I FORGOT THE EGG SHELLS AGAIN!

MISS OTHMAR WILL BE SO UPSET! SHE WANTED US TO BRING EGG SHELLS TO SCHOOL TO MAKE A LITTLE IGLOO VILLAGE...

MISS OTHMAR TAKES HER JOB VERY SERIOUSLY...SHE DOESN'T EVEN LIKE TO BE CALLED A TEACHER...

SHE PREFERS TO BE CALLED AN EDUCATOR!
WOW! HOW SERIOUS CAN YOU GET?
SCHULZ

WELL, DID YOU REMEMBER TO BRING THE EGG SHELLS TODAY, LINUS?

AS SOON AS I WOKE UP THIS MORNING, I THOUGHT TO MYSELF, "HAVE MOM SAVE THE EGG SHELLS WHEN SHE FIXES BREAKFAST!"

SO?

SO TODAY WE HAD COLD CEREAL!
SCHULZ

MISS OTHMAR GOT QUITE UPSET WHEN I TOLD HER I FORGOT THE EGG SHELLS AGAIN TODAY...
SHE TURNED SORT OF PALE AND PUT HER HEAD DOWN ON THE DESK...I THINK SHE MAY EVEN HAVE CRIED A LITTLE...
POOR MISS OTHMAR...I HOPE SHE DOESN'T BECOME ILL...
I NEVER REALIZED IT BEFORE, BUT A SCHOOL TEACHER IS A VERY DELICATE INSTRUMENT!
SCHULZ

..AMEN!

AND PLEASE DON'T LET MISS OTHMAR CRACK UP
SCHULZ

LOOK, CHARLIE BROWN! I FINALLY REMEMBERED THE EGG SHELLS!
YES, SIR, THE OLD BRAIN WAS REALLY FUNCTIONING THIS MORNING! NOW MISS OTHMAR CAN TEACH US ALL ABOUT THOSE IGLOOS...

TODAY IS SATURDAY!

WHAT'S THIS ABOUT YOU AND YOUR TEACHER AND SOME EGG SHELLS?

IT'S JUST LIKE YOU... I'VE NEVER KNOWN ANYONE WHO COULD FORGET THINGS WITH SUCH CLOCKLIKE REGULARITY!

MISS OTHMAR WANTS US TO BRING SOME EGG SHELLS TO SCHOOL TO MAKE IGLOOS, BUT I KEEP FORGETTING...SHE'S VERY UPSET

I GUESS I'M JUST MECHANICALLY MINDED!
SCHULZ

POOR MISS OTHMAR..

I HAD TO GO AND FORGET THE EGG SHELLS AGAIN TODAY.. FOR A MINUTE I THOUGHT SHE WAS GOING TO PASS OUT!

SHE WAS REALLY UPSET, HUH?
I'LL SAY!

SHE HAD A PIECE OF CHALK IN HER HAND, AND WHEN IT SNAPPED, IT SOUNDED LIKE A RIFLE SHOT!
SCHULZ

POOR MISS OTHMAR...
SHE'S GETTING MORE NERVOUS EVERY DAY...I THINK SHE HAS TOO MUCH ON HER MIND....
TEACHERS' MEETINGS, REPORTS TO FILL OUT, PLAYGROUND DUTY PARENT-TEACHER CONFERENCES...
..AND EGG SHELLS..
YEAH, AND EGG SHELLS! SIGH
SCHULZ

IT'S NICE TO BE ABLE TO DOZE OFF FOR A CHANGE WITHOUT ANY WORRIES... IT'S NICE TO KNOW THAT EVERYTHING IS IN GOOD HANDS...

LUCY SAID THAT SHE WOULD SEE TO IT THAT I DON'T FORGET THE EGG SHELLS AGAIN TOMORROW..

Z

DON'T FORGET THE EGG SHELLS!!

SIGH
SCHULZ

I GUESS I JUST DON'T UNDERSTAND DOGS!
?

I CAN'T IMAGINE WHY THEY WANT AN OLD BARE BONE...

SNOOPY'S HAD **THAT** BONE FOR MONTHS, AND YOU NEVER SEE HIM CHEWING ON IT !!

HAS HE NEVER HEARD OF A CONVERSATION PIECE?
SCHULZ

SCHULZ

SNOOP

SCHULZ

YOU KNOW WHAT THEY SHOULD DO ON DECEMBER SIXTEENTH?

THEY SHOULD HAVE A BIG SPECTACULAR ON TV, AND THEY SHOULD CARVE HIS FACE ON MOUNT RUSHMORE!

THEY SHOULD RUN FULL-PAGE ADS IN EVERY NEWSPAPER IN THE COUNTRY WISHING BEETHOVEN A HAPPY BIRTHDAY...

THOSE ARE GOOD IDEAS, LUCY...
THANK YOU... WHEN I GET BIG, I'M GOING TO WORK IN AN ADVERTISING AGENCY!
SCHULZ

SCHROEDER, I JUST WANT YOU TO KNOW THAT I'M ON YOUR SIDE!

I'M SURE I CAN HELP YOU PUBLICITYWISE WITH BEETHOVEN'S BIRTHDAY...

AFTER ALL, THIS IS A REALLY BIG THING....

WE MUST DO WHATEVER IS BEST BEETHOVENWISE!
SCHULZ

DID YOU KNOW THAT DECEMBER 16th IS BEETHOVEN'S BIRTHDAY?
NO, I DIDN'T..

WELL, NOW YOU KNOW!
SCHULZ

HEAR YE! HEAR YE!

THE SIXTEENTH OF DECEMBER IS BEETHOVEN'S BIRTHDAY!

HEAR YE! HEAR YE!

SCHULZ

SCHROEDER, YOU'LL BE PROUD OF THE PUBLICITY JOB I'VE DONE!

JUST THINK, ALL OVER THE COUNTRY PEOPLE WILL BE GATHERED TO RAISE TOASTS, AND SING THEIR BEST WISHES...

I'VE TOLD EVERYONE I KNOW ABOUT BEETHOVEN'S BIRTHDAY BEING THIS WEDNESDAY...

"HAPPY BIRTHDAY, KARL BEETHOVEN!!"
OH, NO!
SCHULZ

LOOK, LUCY, PERHAPS YOU SHOULD KNOW THAT BEETHOVEN'S NAME WASN'T KARL... IT WAS....

OH, NOW YOU'RE GOING TO START PICKING ON ME HUH? AFTER ALL I'VE DONE FOR YOU! TRAMPING THE STREETS, RINGING DOORBELLS...

TALKING TO HUNDREDS OF PEOPLE, TELLING THEM ABOUT BEETHOVEN'S BIRTHDAY!

BUT DO I GET THANKED FOR IT? NO! ALL I GET IS CRITICISM!!!
GOOD GRIEF!
SCHULZ

SCHROEDER, I APOLOGIZE FOR THE WAY I FLEW OFF THE HANDLE YESTERDAY..

TO SHOW THAT MY HEART'S IN THE RIGHT PLACE, I'VE COME OVER TO SING "HAPPY BIRTHDAY" TO BEETHOVEN WITH YOU...OKAY?

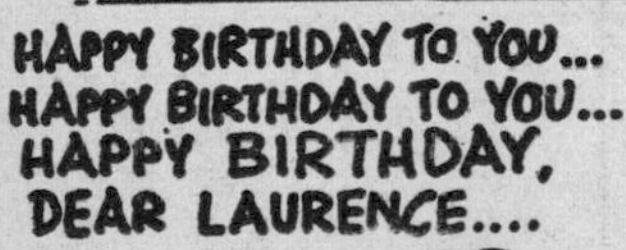
HAPPY BIRTHDAY TO YOU...
HAPPY BIRTHDAY TO YOU...
HAPPY BIRTHDAY,
DEAR LAURENCE....

LAURENCE?
HAPPY BIRTHDAY TO YOOooo!
SCHULZ

OOO, WHAT A FACE!

HE WAS A LOT BETTER LOOKING FROM A DISTANCE!
SCHULZ

GUESS WHAT HAPPENED, CHARLIE BROWN!

I FINALLY REMEMBERED THE EGG SHELLS! I BROUGHT THEM TO SCHOOL, AND GUESS WHAT!

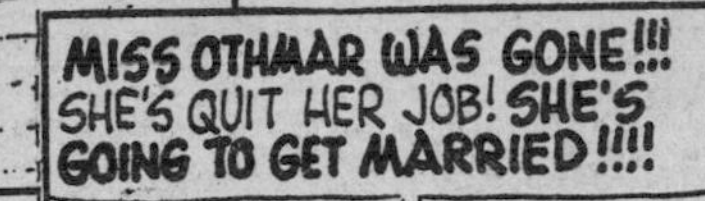
MISS OTHMAR WAS GONE!!! SHE'S QUIT HER JOB! SHE'S GOING TO GET MARRIED!!!!

I KNEW THE EGG SHELLS WERE ONLY A MANIFESTATION OF A DEEPER PROBLEM!

SCHULZ

WHAT IN THE WORLD ARE YOU DOING?

I'M GOING TO SEND MISS OTHMAR A WEDDING PRESENT...

WELL, THAT'S VERY THOUGHTFUL OF YOU, LINUS....WHAT ARE YOU SENDING HER?

A BOX OF EGG SHELLS!
SCHULZ

BOY, THIS WEATHER SURE HAS BEEN TERRIBLE!

WHO CAN WALK TO SCHOOL WHEN IT'S THIS COLD? WHO WANTS TO WALK TO SCHOOL ANYWAY? IN FACT, WHO WANTS TO GO TO SCHOOL?

WHO EVER LEARNS ANYTHING? AND WHAT GOOD DOES IT DO YOU? I'M FED UP WITH THE WHOLE WORKS! I HATE EVERYTHING!

TO PUT A LITTLE FUN IN YOUR LIFE, TRY FUSSING!
SCHULZ

HOW LONG DO YOU THINK IT WILL BE BEFORE SALLY STARTS TO WALK?

GOOD GRIEF! WHAT'S THE HURRY? LET HER CRAWL AROUND FOR AWHILE! DON'T RUSH HER!

SHE'S GOT ALL THE TIME IN THE WORLD...

ONCE YOU STAND UP AND START TO WALK, YOU'RE COMMITTED FOR LIFE!
SCHULZ

THAT'S RIDICULOUS!

OH?

WELL, MAYBE SO...

ALL I KNOW IS IT GIVES US A BETTER PICTURE!
SCHULZ

THE PICTURE'S GETTING FUZZY... RAISE YOUR RIGHT EAR..

SIT UP A LITTLE STRAIGHTER.. MAYBE THAT'LL HELP...

MOVE THAT RIGHT EAR SOME MORE, AND LOWER YOUR LEFT EAR...

THERE!! THAT'S FINE! NOW HOLD IT!
SIGH
SCHULZ

BLAH!

MY MOTHER DIDN'T RAISE ME TO BE A TV AERIAL!
SCHULZ

I WOULDN'T MARRY YOU UNLESS YOU WERE THE LAST GIRL ON EARTH!

DID YOU SAY, "IF" OR "UNLESS"?
I ADMIT I SAID, "UNLESS."...

HOPE!
SCHULZ

I'VE MADE SOME LEMONADE, SNOOPY.

I'M GOING TO LET YOU BE THE FIRST ONE TO TASTE IT...

ALL RIGHT, I'LL ADD A LITTLE MORE SUGAR!
SCHULZ

IT'S THE CHILDREN WHO ARE ALWAYS THE VICTIMS OF SIN AND DISHONOR!

WHENEVER SOMETHING GOES WRONG IN THIS WORLD, IT'S WE CHILDREN WHO SUFFER!

YES, AND DOGS, TOO... DOGS ALSO SUFFER!
THANK YOU!
SCHULZ

I'M SURPRISED THERE'S NO REFUND ON THE EMPTY BOTTLES!
SCHULZ

WHEN I GROW UP, I'D LIKE TO STUDY ABOUT PEOPLE...

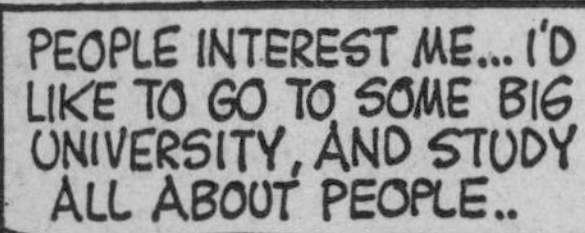
PEOPLE INTEREST ME... I'D LIKE TO GO TO SOME BIG UNIVERSITY, AND STUDY ALL ABOUT PEOPLE..

I SEE...YOU WANT TO LEARN ABOUT PEOPLE SO THAT WITH YOUR KNOWLEDGE YOU WILL BE EQUIPPED TO HELP THEM...

NO, I'M JUST NOSY!
SCHULZ

WHAT IN THE WORLD ARE YOU DOING?
DON'T YOU KNOW?
THIS IS THE TIME OF YEAR WHEN WE ALL WRITE TO THE "GREAT PUMPKIN," AND TELL HIM WHAT WE WANT FOR HALLOWEEN
THE "GREAT PUMPKIN" LOVES LITTLE CHILDREN
I CAN SEE HIM NOW RISING UP OUT OF THE PUMPKIN PATCH WITH HIS BIG BAG OF TOYS!
SCHULZ

HALLOWEEN'S COMING, CHARLIE BROWN!

I'VE WRITTEN A LETTER TO THE "GREAT PUMPKIN" TELLING HIM WHAT I WANT HIM TO BRING ME...
IF YOU HAVEN'T WRITTEN TO HIM YET, CHARLIE BROWN, YOU'D BETTER HURRY!

OH, I LOVE THIS TIME OF YEAR! EVERYONE'S SO FULL OF JOY AND GOOD WILL!
SCHULZ

WHY DON'T WE GET THE WHOLE GANG TOGETHER, AND GO OUT AND SING PUMPKIN CAROLS?
SCHULZ

...AND THEN ON HALLOWEEN NIGHT THE "GREAT PUMPKIN" RISES UP OUT OF THE PUMPKIN PATCH...

..AND HE BRINGS TOYS TO ALL THE GOOD LITTLE CHILDREN IN THE WORLD!
YOU'RE CRAZY!

ALL RIGHT, SO YOU BELIEVE IN SANTA CLAUS, AND I'LL BELIEVE IN THE "GREAT PUMPKIN"..
THE WAY I SEE IT, IT DOESN'T MATTER WHAT YOU BELIEVE, JUST SO YOU'RE SINCERE!
SCHULZ

TOMORROW NIGHT IS OUR BIG NIGHT, LINUS..

ALL YOU HAVE TO DO IS WALK UP TO A HOUSE, RING THE DOORBELL AND SAY, "TRICKS OR TREATS!"

ARE YOU SURE THAT'S LEGAL?
OF COURSE, IT'S LEGAL!
GOOD...I WOULDN'T WANT TO BE ACCUSED OF TAKING PART IN A RUMBLE!
SCHULZ

WELL, WHAT'S THE MATTER WITH YOU?

YOU DIDN'T TELL ME YOU WERE GOING TO KILL IT!
SCHULZ

WELL, HALLOWEEN HAS COME AND GONE...
SO IT HAS

DID THE "GREAT PUMPKIN" BRING YOU LOTS OF NICE PRESENTS?
OH, SHUT UP!
SCHULZ

LOOK AT ME.. I'M THE "GREAT PUMPKIN"!

I RISE UP OUT OF THE PUMPKIN PATCH, AND BRING TOYS TO ALL THE CHILDREN ON HALLOWEEN!

HEY, LINUS! HOW MANY TOYS DID HE BRING YOU?!!
HA HA HA HA HA!!!

I WAS A VICTIM OF FALSE DOCTRINE..
SCHULZ

SIGH
SCHULZ

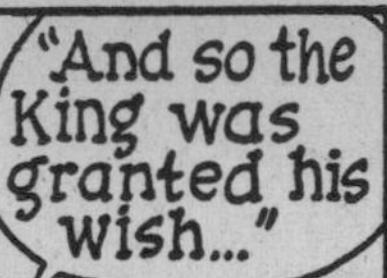
"And so the King was granted his wish..."

"Everything he touched would turn to gold! Now, the next day..."

STOP! YOU DON'T HAVE TO READ ANY FURTHER! I KNOW JUST WHAT'S GOING TO HAPPEN..

THESE THINGS ALWAYS HAVE A WAY OF BACKFIRING!
SCHULZ

YOU'RE A FOOL, CHARLIE BROWN!
I DON'T KNOW WHY I WASTE MY TIME EVEN TALKING TO YOU!
AH-CHOOO!

SCHULZ
I THINK I'M BECOMING ALLERGIC TO CRITICISM!

SCHULZ

SUDDENLY I FEEL LIKE THE PIED PIPER!

YOU'RE WEAK! YOU'RE A REAL JELLYFISH!

YOU'RE DUMB, YOU'RE STUPID YOU'RE IGNORANT AND YOU HAVE A SILLY FACE!

POOR CHARLIE BROWN... I SEE THE CATS HAVE BEEN USING YOU TO SHARPEN THEIR CLAWS AGAIN, HUH?

YEAH, I'M SORT OF A SPIRITUAL SCRATCHING POST!
SCHULZ

IT'S NICE TO WAKE UP IN THE MORNING WITH A FEELING OF WELL-BEING..

TO KNOW THAT EVEN THOUGH THERE'S SNOW ON THE GROUND AND IT'S A LITTLE CHILLY OUTSIDE, BASICALLY LIFE IS GOOD, AND THAT YOU PERSONALLY ARE...

?
SNOOPY

DOOMED!
SCHULZ

GOOD GRIEF! TRAPPED IN A DOGHOUSE BY AN ICICLE!
SNOOPY

I'LL BET IF I MAKE JUST THE SLIGHTEST MOVE, IT'LL CRASH DOWN, AND KILL ME!
SNOOPY

I DON'T WANT TO DIE! I'M TOO **YOUNG** TO DIE! I'M TOO **NICE** TO DIE!
SNOOPY

SCHULZ
I'M TOO **ME** TO DIE!!

IT'S SILLY TO BE TRAPPED IN A DOGHOUSE BY AN ICICLE!
SNOOPY

I THINK I'LL JUST MAKE A RUN FOR IT! I THINK I'LL JUST ZOOM OUT OF HERE!
SNOOPY

I THINK I'LL JUST LEAP UP, AND ZOOM RIGHT OUT!
SNOOPY

SCHULZ
I THINK I'LL JUST LIE HERE FOR THE REST OF MY LIFE!
SNOOPY

LOOKS BAD, DOESN'T IT?
TERRIBLE!
SNOOPY

YOU KNOW WHAT I'VE HEARD?
NO, WHAT HAVE YOU HEARD?
SNOOPY

I'VE HEARD THAT LOUD NOISES WILL SOMETIMES CAUSE AN ICICLE TO FALL...
SNOOPY

IS THAT RIGHT?
SCHULZ

I'M DOOMED!
SNOOPY

HELLO, HUMANE SOCIETY? WE NEED YOUR ADVICE...HOW DO YOU GET A DOG OUT OF A DOGHOUSE BEFORE AN ICICLE FALLS ON HIM?

HE SAID TO TRY COAXING HIM OUT WITH HIS FAVORITE FOOD... SOMETHING HE JUST CAN'T RESIST...

WHAT'S THE NUMBER OF "VILLELLA'S TAKE-OUT PIZZA PARLOR"?
SCHULZ

I'M DOING JUST WHAT THE MAN FROM THE HUMANE SOCIETY SAID TO DO...

SNIF? SNIF? SNIF?
?
SNOOPY

ZOOM
WHAM!

SAVED BY A PIZZA!
GOOD GRIEF!
SCHULZ

DEAR SANTA CLAUS,
IT HAS COME TO OUR ATTENTION THAT YOU BASE YOUR GIVING ON THE DEPORTMENT OF THE INDIVIDUAL CHILD...

IN OTHER WORDS, YOU JUDGE AS TO WHETHER THE CHILD HAS BEEN GOOD OR BAD...DO YOU REALLY THINK IT IS WISE TO ATTEMPT TO PASS SUCH JUDGMENT?
WHAT IS GOOD? WHAT IS BAD? CAN WE SAY TO OUR NEIGHBOR, "YOU ARE BAD...I AM GOOD"? CAN WE SAY...
OH, BROTHER!
SCHULZ

TO GO FURTHER INTO THIS MATTER OF THE GIFTS YOU BEAR, DEAR SANTA...

IF, PERCHANCE, YOU JUDGE A LITTLE CHILD AS TOO 'BAD' TO RECEIVE ANY TOYS, ARE YOU NOT ALSO JUDGING HIS PARENTS?

AND IF YOU JUDGE THE PARENTS, THEN ARE YOU NOT ALSO JUDGING THE REMAINDER OF THE FAMILY, THE INNOCENT BROTHERS OR SISTERS, AS THE CASE MAY BE?

IN OTHER WORDS DEAR SANTA, MUST I SUFFER FOR THE DEEDS OF...
AH, HA!
SCHULZ

I HEARD WHAT YOU WERE SAYING IN THAT LETTER! A FINE BROTHER YOU TURNED OUT TO BE!

LOOK, I WAS ONLY TRYING TO TELL SANTA CLAUS THAT I DIDN'T THINK HE SHOULD PASS UP OUR HOUSE, AND NOT LEAVE ME ANY PRESENTS JUST BECAUSE OF YOU!

IF HE THINKS YOU'VE BEEN BAD ALL YEAR, WHY SHOULD I SUFFER?

DON'T LOOK AT ME...I'M ONLY THE SECRETARY!
SCHULZ

YOU AND YOUR LETTERS TO SANTA CLAUS!

YOU THINK YOU CAN GET ME IN BAD WITH HIM, BUT YOU CAN'T! SANTA IS VERY FORGIVING WITH LITTLE GIRLS!
OH, YEAH?

YEAH! LITTLE GIRLS CAN GET AWAY WITH A LOT MORE THAN LITTLE BOYS!
WHAT MAKES YOU THINK SO?

BECAUSE WE'RE SO CUTE!
SCHULZ

YOU FOOL!

YOU BLOCKHEAD! YOU NITWIT!! YOU NUMSKULL!!!

DO YOU THINK HE HEARD YOU?
I'M SURE HE DID..

INSULTS SEEM TO TRAVEL FARTHER WHEN THE AIR IS THIN!
SCHULZ

cresc.
SCHULZ

SURE, I THINK DOGS SHOULD BE TREATED KINDLY...

I'VE ALWAYS BELIEVED IN BEING KIND TO ANIMALS..

AND I THINK WE SHOULD DO ALL WE CAN TO MAKE OUR PETS HAPPY...

BUT **THIS** IS RIDICULOUS!!

WHERE IN THE WORLD IS LINUS? WE'RE GOING TO BE LATE FOR THE SHOW!
HE BROKE A SHOELACE, AND HAD TO GO BACK TO TRY TO FIND ANOTHER...

I THINK HE'S TAKING ONE OUT OF HIS DAD'S HUNTING BOOTS..
SCHULZ
OKAY, I'M ALL SET TO GO!

THERE'S NO USE ARGUING ABOUT IT! I'D LIKE TO PLAY, BUT I **CAN'T**!

MY MOTHER TOLD ME TO PUSH SALLY AROUND IN HER STROLLER, AND THAT'S WHAT I'M GOING TO DO! IT'S WHAT I **HAVE** TO DO!

WELL, YOU'VE GOT TO ADMIT THAT IT'S THAT KIND OF DEVOTION THAT BUILDS CHARACTER...
...AND **LOSES** BALL GAMES!
SCHULZ

CHARLIE BROWN CAN'T MANAGE OUR TEAM TODAY BECAUSE HE HAS TO PUSH HIS BABY SISTER AROUND IN HER STROLLER!
HE WHAT?

IS THIS TRUE?!!
I CAN'T LOOK HIM IN THE EYE!
SCHULZ

I HOPE SHE'S **SATISFIED**!
ALL BECAUSE SHE HAS TO RIDE AROUND IN HER OL' STROLLER! **WELL, I JUST HOPE SHE'S SATISFIED!**

DEPRIVING US OF A MANAGER JUST BEFORE OUR LAST AND MOST CRUCIAL GAME!
MY FIRST YEAR IN THIS WORLD, AND ALREADY I HAVE **GUILT** FEELINGS!
SCHULZ

THERE'S MY BASEBALL TEAM OUT THERE GETTING CLOBBERED..

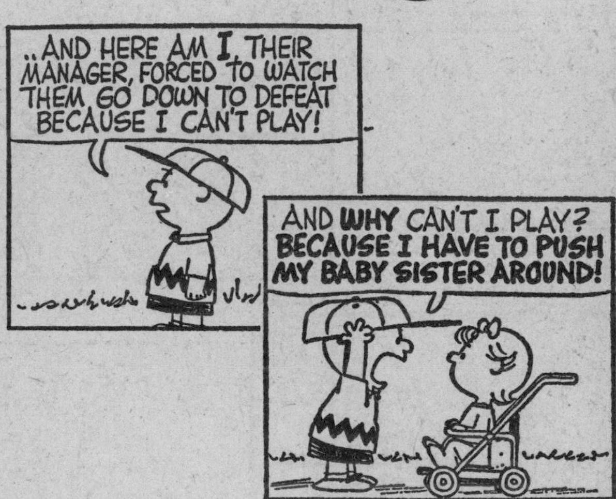
..AND HERE AM I, THEIR MANAGER, FORCED TO WATCH THEM GO DOWN TO DEFEAT BECAUSE I CAN'T PLAY!
AND WHY CAN'T I PLAY? BECAUSE I HAVE TO PUSH MY BABY SISTER AROUND!

SCHULZ
NOBODY LIKES ME!

HAVE THE INFIELD MOVE IN, AND TRY TO CUT OFF THE RUN AT THE PLATE...

I SHOULD BE BACK HERE IN ABOUT FIVE MINUTES..

GOOD GRIEF!

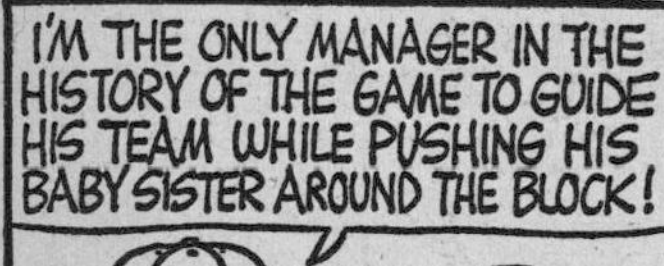
I'M THE ONLY MANAGER IN THE HISTORY OF THE GAME TO GUIDE HIS TEAM WHILE PUSHING HIS BABY SISTER AROUND THE BLOCK!

SIGH
SCHULZ

WELL, HOW'S THE GAME GOING?

WE'VE STILL GOT A CHANCE, CHARLIE BROWN, BUT WE NEED **YOU**! DON'T YOU THINK YOU'VE PUSHED SALLY LONG ENOUGH?

YOU'RE RIGHT! I'LL RUSH HER HOME, AND ZOOM BACK HERE IN TIME TO **WIN** THE GAME!
DIG OUT, MAN!
SCHULZ

I'M SORRY I CAN'T PUSH YOU ANY MORE, SALLY, BUT I HAVE TO GO SAVE MY TEAM FROM DEFEAT

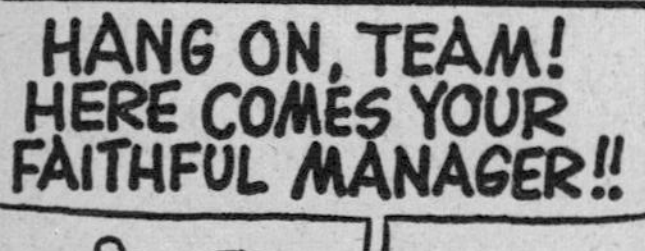
HANG ON, TEAM! HERE COMES YOUR FAITHFUL MANAGER!!

I HAD NO IDEA THAT LIFE WAS GOING TO BE FILLED WITH SUCH DRAMA..
SCHULZ

HERE COMES GOOD OL' CHARLIE BROWN!
HE MUST BE THROUGH PUSHING HIS BABY SISTER!

YOU'RE JUST IN TIME TO GO IN AS A PINCH-HITTER, OL' BUDDY! YOU CAN SAVE THE GAME, OL' PAL!

REMEMBER, OL' BUDDY, WE'RE COUNTING ON YOU!
BE A HERO, CHARLIE BROWN, OL' PAL!

OR DON'T SHOW YOUR FACE AROUND HERE AGAIN!
SCHULZ

IT'S HERO TIME!

THIS IS MY BIG CHANCE TO BE A HERO!

I'M TIRED OF ALWAYS BEING THE GOAT..

STRIKE ONE!
GOOD GRIEF!
SCHULZ

EVERYONE HAS THE POTENTIALITIES OF A HERO OR A GOAT LYING WITHIN HIM...

STRIKE TWO!
I CAN FEEL THE **GOAT** IN ME RISING TO THE SURFACE!
SCHULZ

IT ONLY TAKES ONE TO HIT IT...
THE GAME IS NEVER OVER UNTIL THE LAST MAN IS OUT! I CAN STILL BE A HERO..

IT ONLY TAKES ONE TO HIT IT.. IT ONLY TAKES ONE TO HIT IT!
STRIKE THREE!
THAT WASN'T THE ONE!
SCHULZ

I THINK I'M GOING TO CRY..
SCHULZ

WHOEVER TOLD YOU THAT YOU COULD PLAY BASEBALL?! YOU'RE THE WORLD'S WORST! YOU'RE USELESS! YOU'RE TERRIBLE!

SAY, THIS IS WHERE I LIVE..
OH, YES, SO IT IS...

WELL, DON'T WORRY..I'VE STILL GOT A LITTLE WAY TO GO SO I CAN TAKE OVER...

WHOEVER TOLD YOU THAT YOU COULD PLAY BASEBALL? YOU'RE NO GOOD FOR ANYTHING! YOU'RE WORSE THAN USELESS! YOU'RE WORSE THAN TERRIBLE! YOU'RE..
SCHULZ

THIS IS THE WORST YET..I'VE REALLY HIT BOTTOM!

MY MOTHER IS MAD AT ME FOR RUNNING OUT ON MY JOB OF PUSHING MY BABY SISTER AROUND IN HER STROLLER...

AND NOW ALL THE KIDS ARE MAD AT ME FOR STRIKING OUT AND LOSING THE BIGGEST GAME OF THE SEASON!

SUDDENLY I FEEL VERY OLD...
SCHULZ

LIFE IS JUST TOO MUCH FOR ME..

I'VE BEEN CONFUSED RIGHT FROM THE DAY I WAS BORN...
I THINK THE WHOLE TROUBLE IS THAT WE'RE THROWN INTO LIFE TOO FAST...WE'RE NOT REALLY PREPARED...

WHAT DID YOU WANT...A CHANCE TO WARM UP FIRST?
SCHULZ

LOOK, I SACRIFICED A LOT TO COME BACK AND PLAY IN THAT GAME!

I WAS SUPPOSED TO BE PUSHING MY BABY SISTER IN HER STROLLER...NOW MY MOTHER'S MAD AT ME!

BUT I DID IT FOR OUR TEAM! DO YOU UNDERSTAND THAT? I SACRIFICED MYSELF FOR OUR TEAM! DO YOU UNDERSTAND THAT, LUCY? DO YOU?

I WONDER WHAT BIRDS THINK ABOUT WHEN THEY FLY AROUND UP THERE!
SCHULZ

DID BEETHOVEN EVER ROLL A "THREE HUNDRED" GAME?

YOU MEAN IN BOWLING? GOOD GRIEF, HOW IN THE WORLD SHOULD I KNOW?!

I THOUGHT YOU WERE AN AUTHORITY ON BEETHOVEN!
SCHULZ

I'VE BEEN FEELING PRETTY DISCOURAGED THE LAST FEW DAYS, SALLY..

BUT IT'S REALLY ALL MY OWN FAULT... I GUESS I ALSO OWE YOU AN APOLOGY FOR ALL THE COMPLAINING I DID JUST BECAUSE I HAD TO TAKE YOU OUT FOR A WALK

MAYBE IF YOU AND I STICK TOGETHER AS BROTHER AND SISTER WE CAN LICK THIS OLD WORLD YET! WHAT DO YOU SAY?

I'LL DRINK TO THAT!
SCHULZ

SCHULZ

LOOK, CHARLIE BROWN! A LETTER FROM MISS OTHMAR!

ONLY HER NAME ISN'T OTHMAR ANY MORE...IT'S MRS. HAGEMEYER! SHE THANKS ME FOR THE EGG SHELLS I SENT, AND SAYS SHE'LL KEEP THEM FOREVER...

AND SHE SAYS SHE MISSES ALL THE KIDS IN HER CLASS, BUT YOU KNOW WHO SHE SAYS SHE MISSES MOST? ME!!

SCHULZ

ONLY 28 MORE DAYS UNTIL BEETHOVEN'S BIRTHDAY!
WHERE **DOES** THE TIME GO?
SCHULZ

Z
Z

Z
ALL RIGHT, WHO'S THE WISE GUY?
SCHULZ

And don't forget about
all the other PEANUTS
books in CORONET Book
editions. Good Grief!
More than EIGHT MILLION
of them in paperback!
See the check-list overleaf.

Wherever Paperbacks Are Sold